THE ULTIMATE SONGLIST

Designed by Chloë Alexander Design

© 2014 by Faber Music Ltd
First published by Faber Music Ltd in 2014
Bloomsbury House
74-77 Great Russell Street
London WC1B 3DA

Printed in England by Caligraving Ltd
All rights reserved

This paper is 100% recyclable

ISBN: 0-571-53876-2
EAN: 978-0-571-53876-8

To buy Faber Music publications or to find out about the full range of titles available,
please contact your local music retailer or Faber Music sales enquiries:

Faber Music Limited, Burnt Mill, Elizabeth Way, Harlow CM20 2HX
Tel: +44 (0)1279 82 89 82
Fax: +44 (0)1279 82 89 83

FABER ff MUSIC

ALMOST LOVER

Words and Music by Alison Sudol

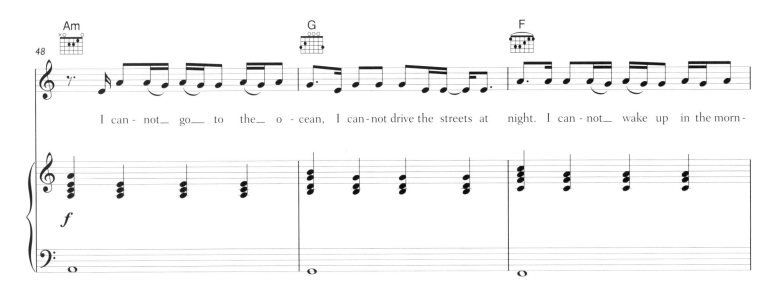

I can - not_ go_ to the_ o - cean, I can - not drive the streets at night. I can - not_ wake up in the morn-

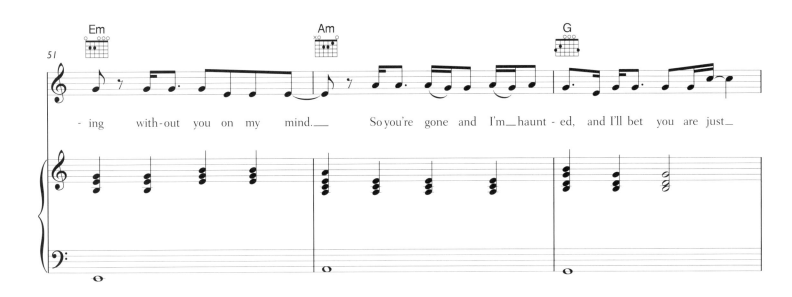

- ing with - out you on my mind.__ So you're gone and I'm_ haunt - ed, and I'll bet you are just_

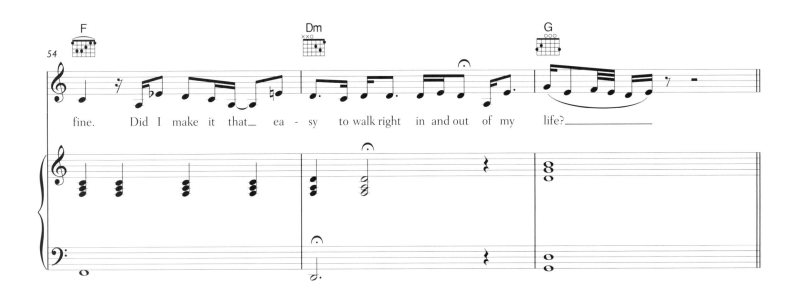

fine. Did I make it that_ ea - sy to walk right in and out of my life?_____

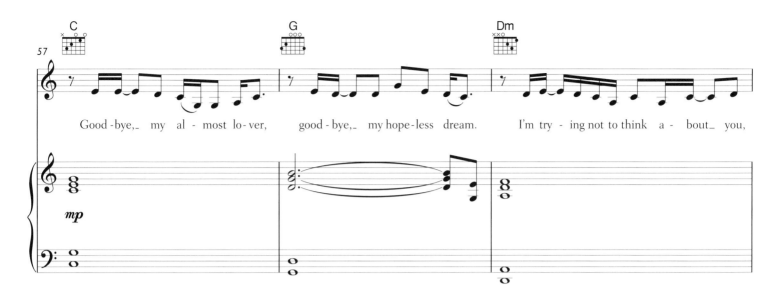

Good -bye,_ my al - most lo-ver, good - bye,_ my hope-less dream. I'm try - ing not to think a - bout_ you,

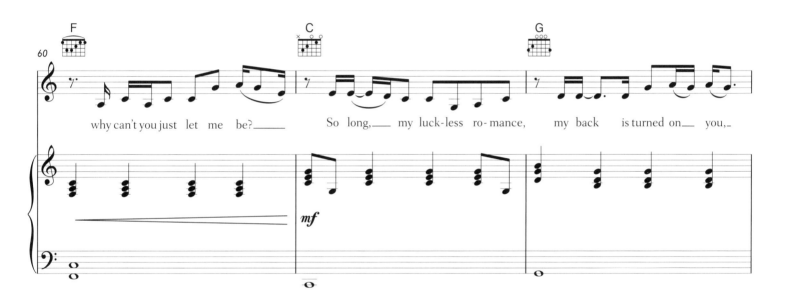

why can't you just let me be?_____ So long,___ my luck-less ro-mance, my back is turned on___ you,_

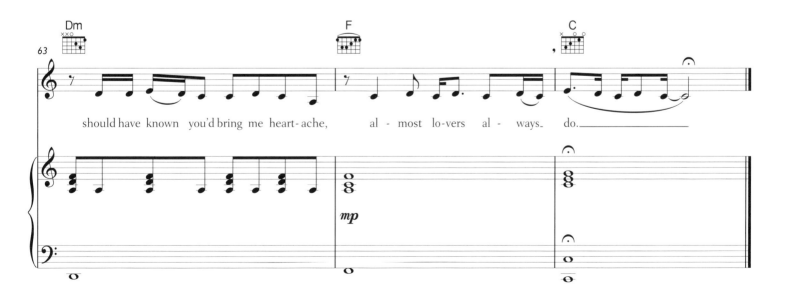

should have known you'd bring me heart-ache, al - most lo-vers al - ways_ do._____

ANOTHER LOVE

Words and Music by Tom Odell

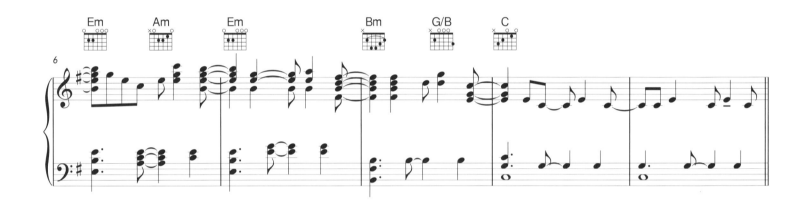

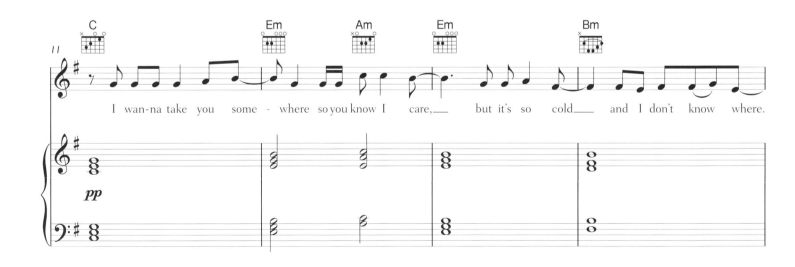

I wan-na take you some - where so you know I care,___ but it's so cold___ and I don't know where.

I wan-na sing a song___ that -'ll be just ours___ but I sang 'em all___ to an-oth-er heart.

___ And I wan-na cry,___ I wan-na fall in love,___ but all my tears___ have been used up___

up.___

BEST SONG EVER

Words and Music by Wayne Hector, Edward Drewett, Julian C Bunetta and John Ryan

1. May-be it's the way she walked____ straight in-to my heart and stole it,
2. Said her name was Geor-gia Rose,____ and her dad-dy was a den-tist,

BEWITCHED

Words by Lorenz Hart
Music by Richard Rodgers

CREEP

**Words and Music by Thomas Yorke, Jonathan Greenwood, Colin Greenwood,
Edward O'Brien, Philip Selway, Albert Hammond and Mike Hazelwood**

CRY ME A RIVER

Words and Music by Arthur Hamilton

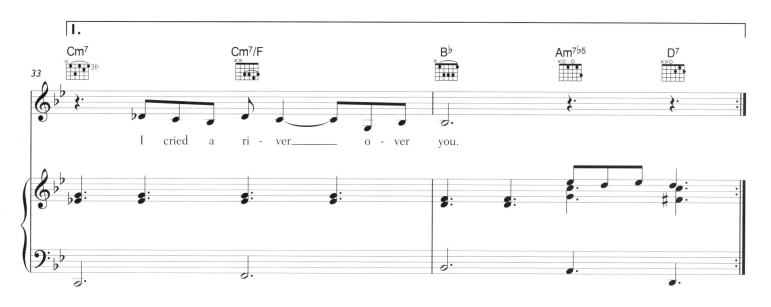

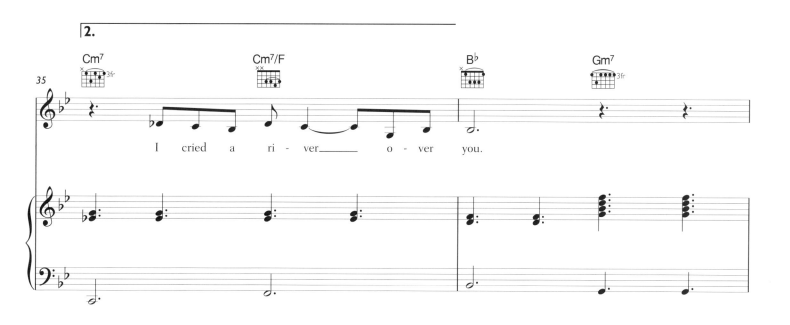

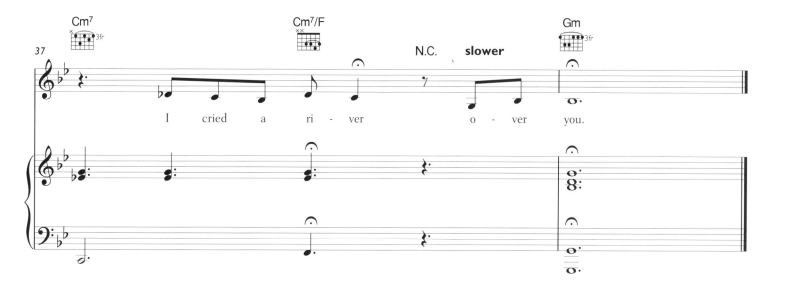

DEAR DARLIN'

Words and Music by Edward Drewett, James Eliot and Olly Murs

DON'T STOP BELIEVIN'

Words and Music by Jonathan Cain, Neal Schon and Stephen Perry

EMPIRE STATE OF MIND (PART II) BROKEN DOWN

**Words and Music by Sylvia Robinson, Bert Keyes, Shawn Carter,
Angela Hunte, Alicia Augello-Cook, Janet Sewell and Al Shuckburgh**

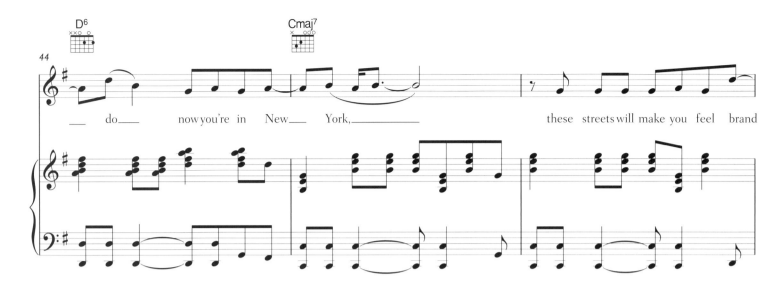

do___ now you're in New___ York,_____ these streets will make you feel brand

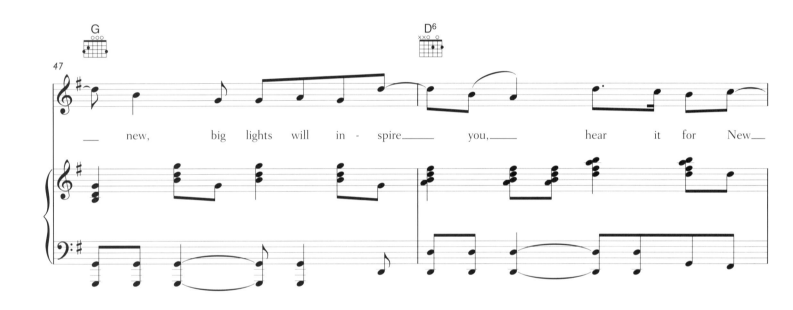

___ new, big lights will in - spire_____ you,____ hear it for New___

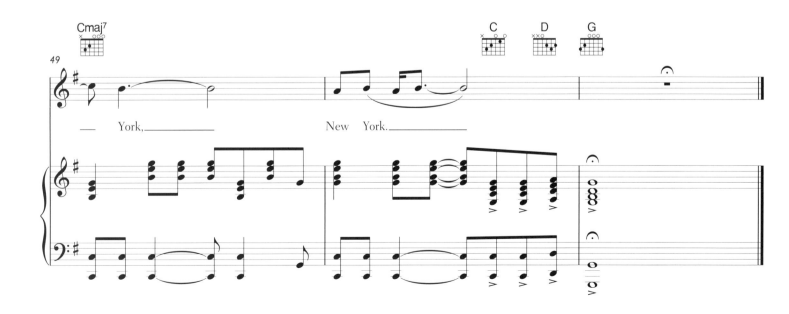

___ York,_____ New York._____

GET HAPPY

Words and Music by Harold Arlen and Ted Koehler

GONE

Words and Music by Lianne Barnes and Matthew Hales

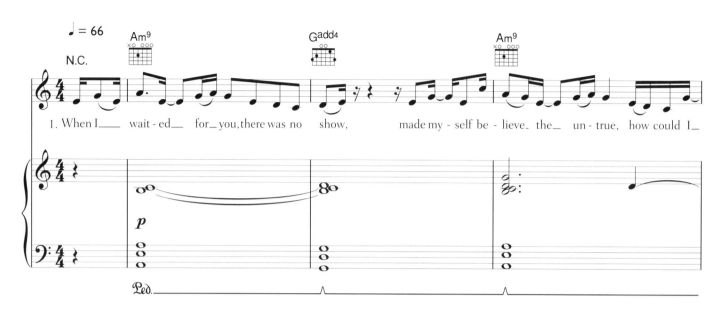

1. When I___ wait-ed___ for___ you, there was no show, made my-self be-lieve___ the___ un-true, how could I

___ not___ know? I bet it seemed eas-ier_____ just to lie,_____ but I found you out,___ this is___

___ my___ last good-bye. I heard e-nough fair-y-tales back in my youth, so just___ stop bit-

GRAN TORINO (MAIN TITLE)

Words and Music by Kyle C Eastwood, Michael C. Stevens, Clint Eastwood and Jamie Cullum

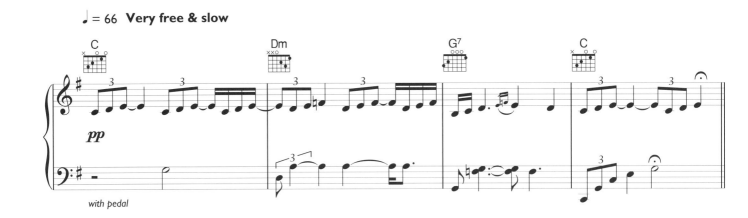

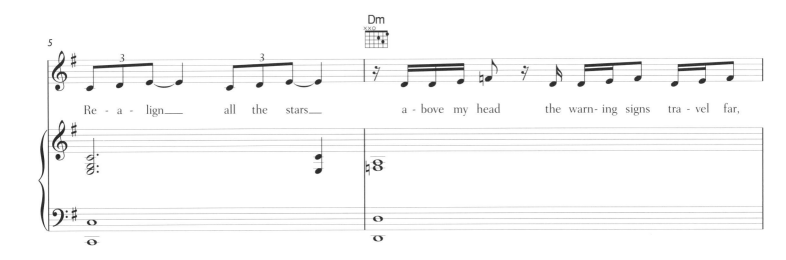

Re-a-lign___ all the stars___ a-bove my head the warn-ing signs tra-vel far,

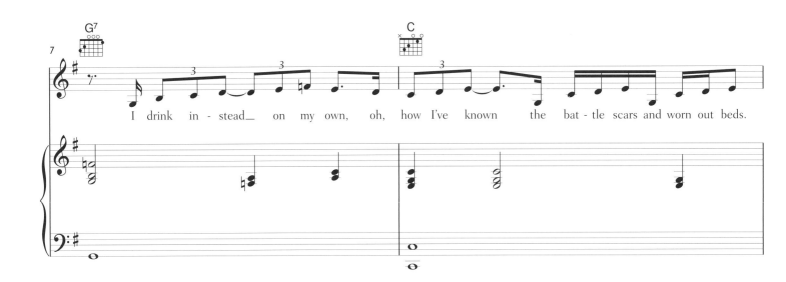

I drink in-stead___ on my own, oh, how I've known the bat-tle scars and worn out beds.

HIDING MY HEART

Words and Music by Timothy Hanseroth

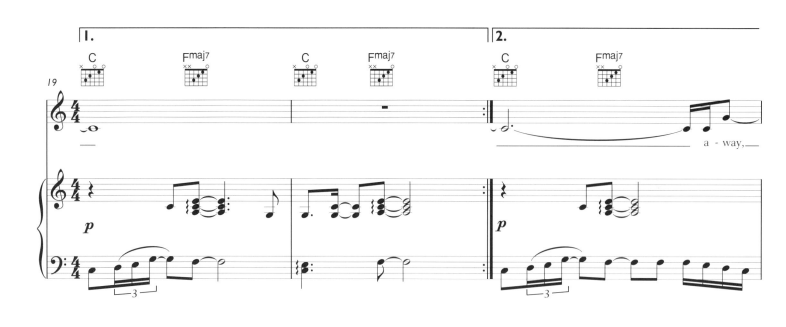

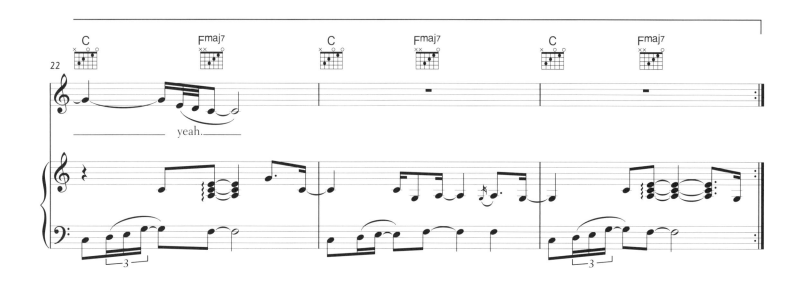

yeah.

I can't spend my whole life hid - ing my heart___ a - way.

HIGH HOPES

Words and Music by Mark Prendergast, Vincent May and Stephen Garrigan

HO HEY

Words and Music by Jeremy Fraites and Wesley Schultz

HOLD ON

Words and Music by Michael Bublé, Alan Chang and Amy Foster-Gillies

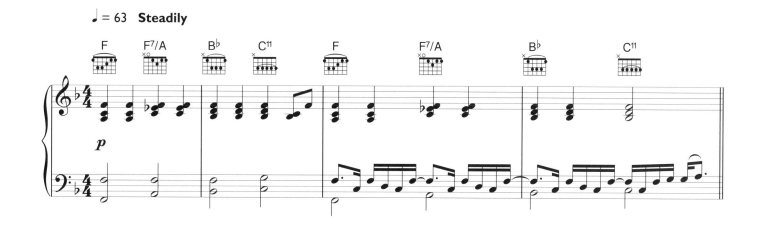

1. Didn't they al-ways say___ we were the luck-y ones? I guess that we were once,___ babe, we
2. There's a thou-sand ways___ for things to fall a-part, but it's no-one's fault, no, it's

were once.___
not our fault.   But luck will leave you cursed, it is a faith-less friend and
And may-be all the plans we made might not work out, but I

ICH WILL NUR

Words and Music by Frank Pilsl and Philipp Poisel

1. Ver-steck mich wo du mich nicht find - est, da - mit auch du mich mal ver-misst,

die   mich so   voll- en - det,

die   mich so_____   be - wegt._____

To Coda ⊕

1.

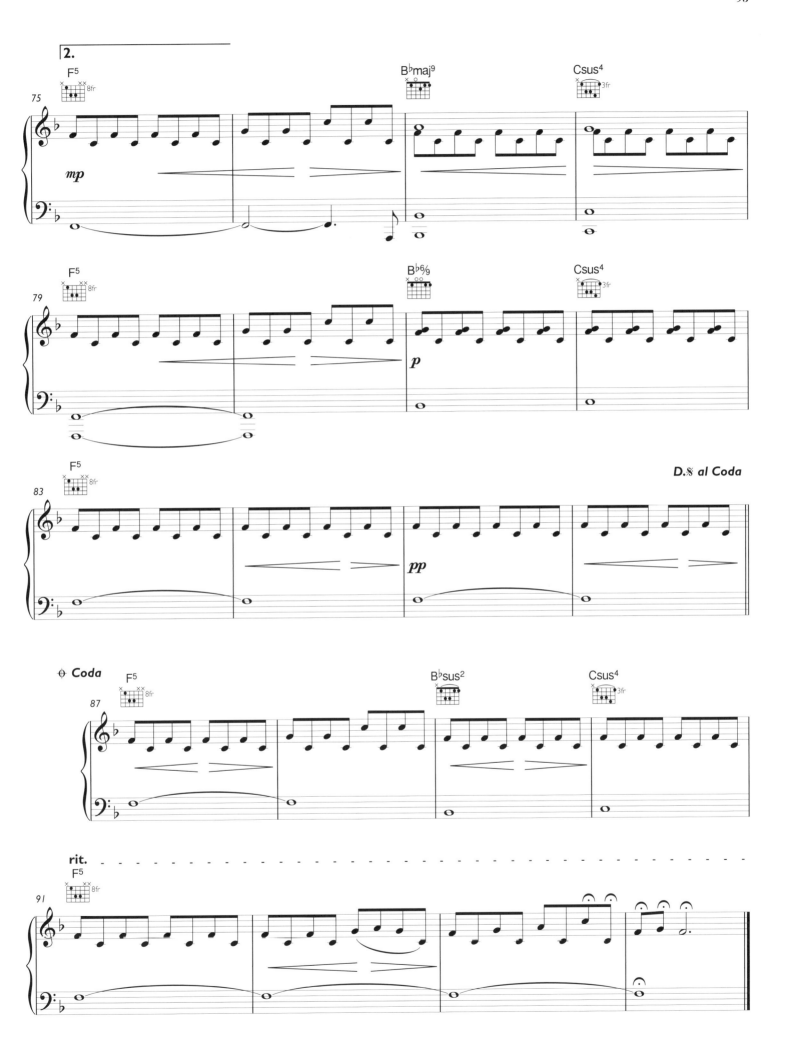

I SAY A LITTLE PRAYER

Music by Burt Bacharach
Words by Hal David

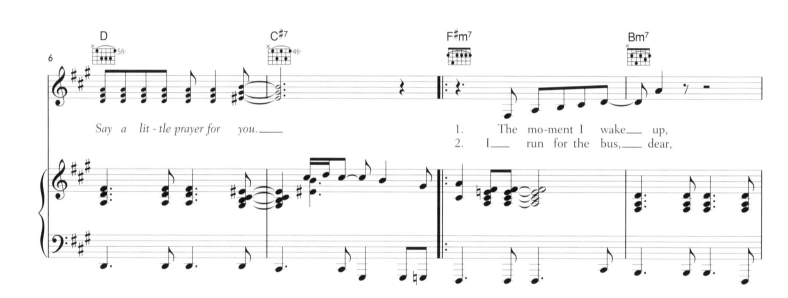

Say a lit - tle prayer for you.____

1. The mo - ment I wake__ up,
2. I__ run for the bus,__ dear,

be - fore I put   on__ my__ make - up, *(make - up)* I say a lit - tle *prayer for* *you.*
but while ri - ding I   think_ of__ us, dear, *(us dear)* I say a lit - tle *prayer for* *you.*

96

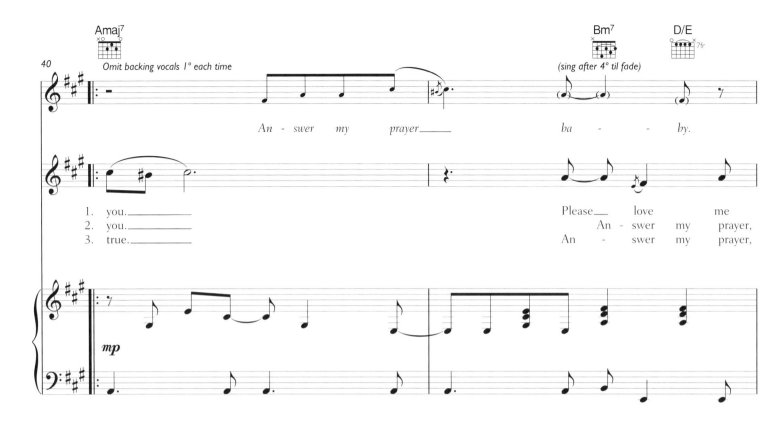

JUST GIVE ME A REASON

Words and Music by Nathaniel Joseph Ruess, Alecia Moore and Jeffrey Bhasker

LAST CHRISTMAS

Words and Music by George Michael

1. Once bit - ten and twice shy_____ I keep my dis - tance but
2. A crowd - ed room, friends with tir - ed eyes, I'm hid - ing from you

you still catch_ my eye,_____ tell me ba - by, do you re - cog - nise me?
and your soul_ of ice. My God! I thought you were some - one to re - ly on.

Well, it's been a year, it does - n't sur - prise_ me. Happy Christmas... I
Me? I guess I was a shoul - der to cry_ on. A face on a lov - er with a

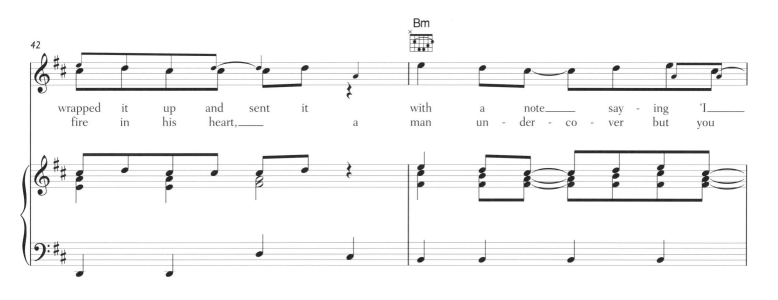

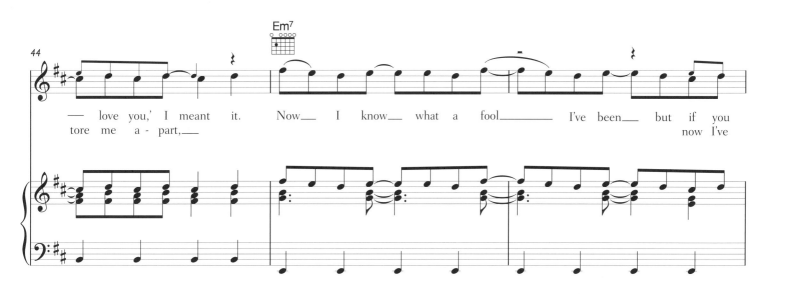

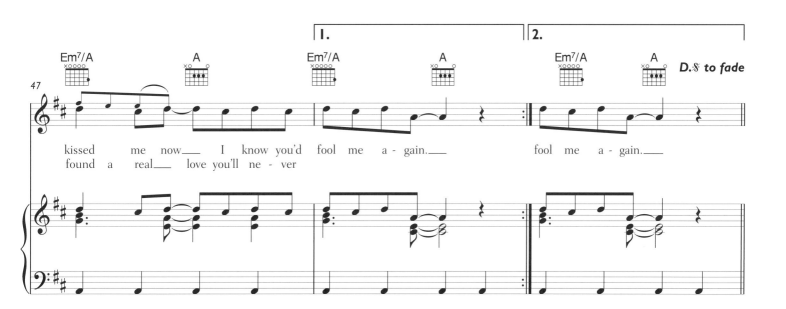

LEGO HOUSE

Words and Music by Christopher Leonard, Ed Sheeran and Jake Gosling

LIEDER

**Words and Music by Sebastian Wehlings,
Tobias Kuhn, Sebastian Kirchner and Adel Tawil**

LET IT GO (FROM 'FROZEN')

Words and Music by Robert Lopez and Kristen Anderson-Lopez

THE LIFE I NEVER LED (REPRISE)

Words and Music by Alan Menken and Glenn Slater

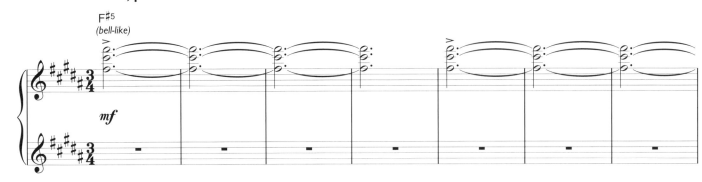

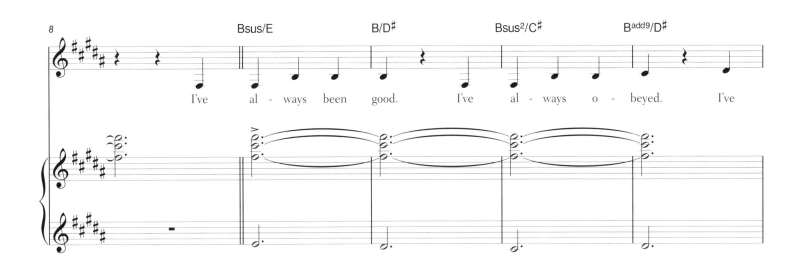

I've al-ways been good. I've al-ways o-beyed. I've

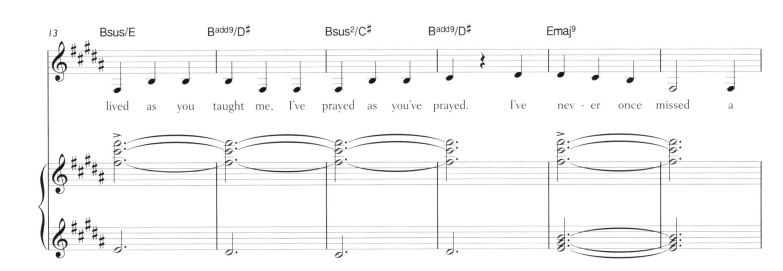

lived as you taught me, I've prayed as you've prayed. I've nev-er once missed a

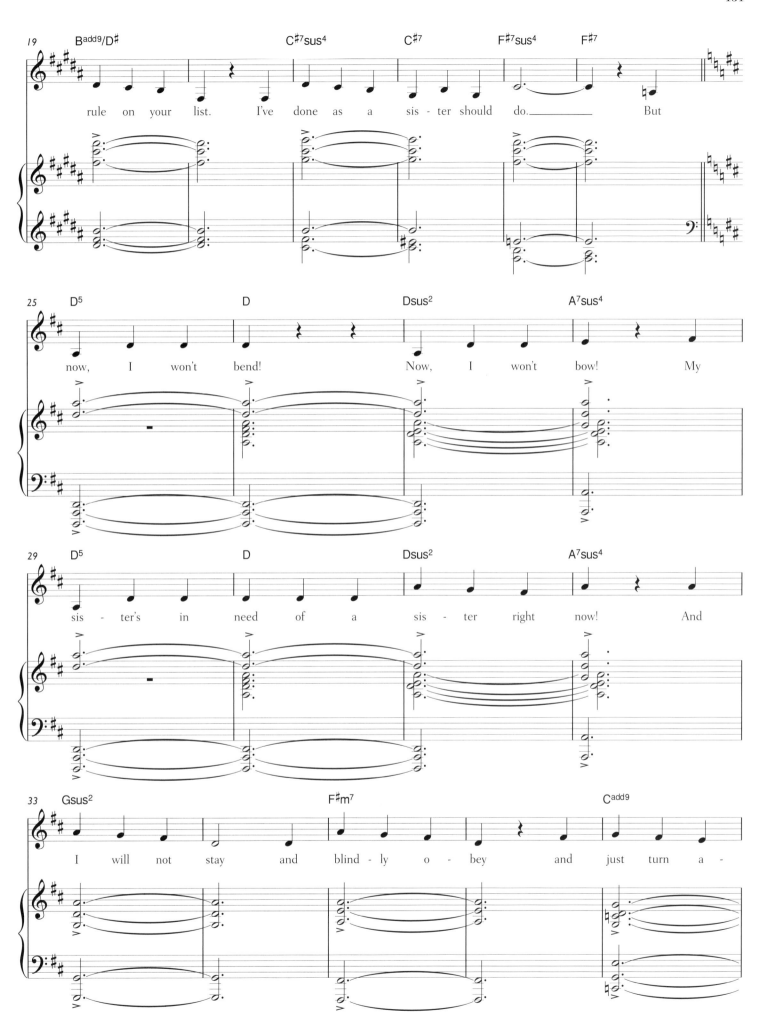

LIKE A PRAYER

Words and Music by Madonna and Pat Leonard

NOT ABOUT ANGELS

Words and Music by Jasmine van den Bogaerde

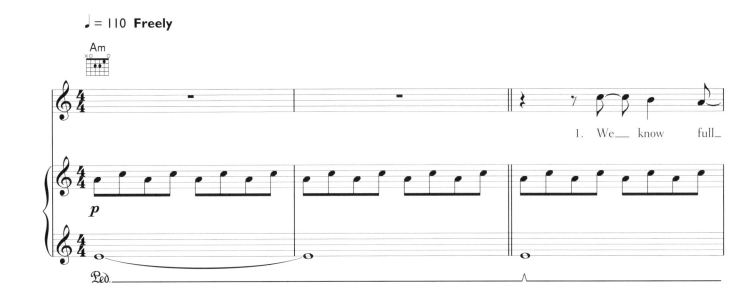

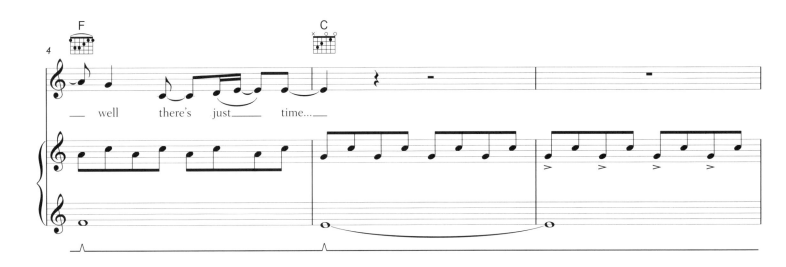

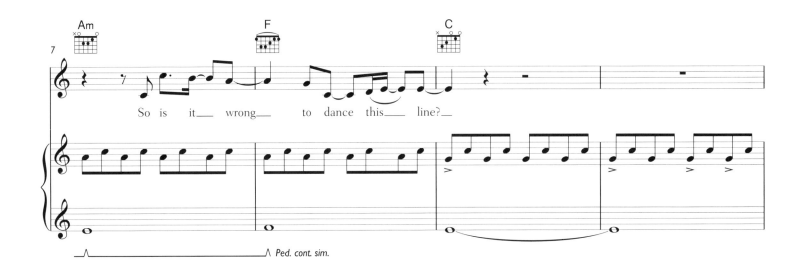

ONE DAY LIKE THIS

Words and Music by Guy Garvey, Craig Potter, Mark Potter, Peter Turner and Richard Jupp

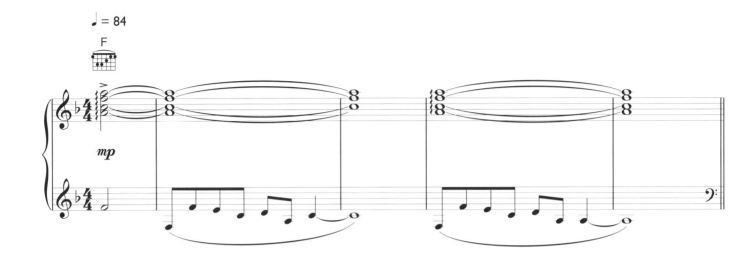

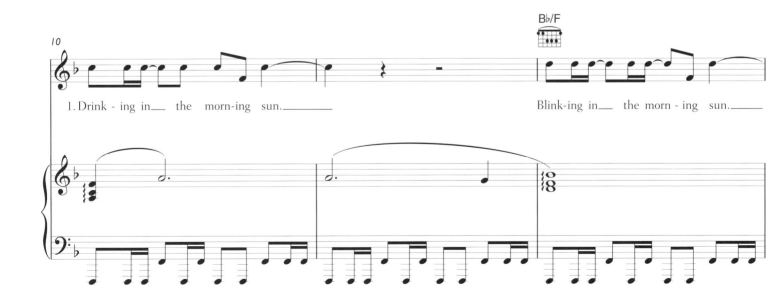

1. Drink - ing in__ the morn-ing sun._____

Blink-ing in__ the morn - ing sun.__

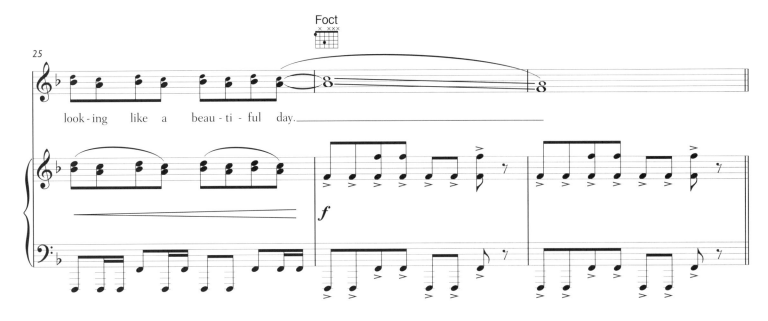

look-ing   like   a   beau-ti-ful   day.

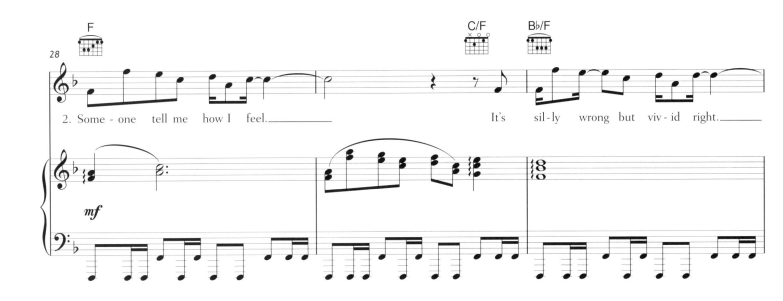

2. Some-one   tell me   how I   feel._____   It's   sil-ly   wrong but   viv-id   right._____

_____   Oh,   kiss me like_ a   fin - al   meal._____   Yeah,

THE POWER OF LOVE

Words and Music by Mark O'Toole, Brian Nash, Holly Johnson and Peter Gill

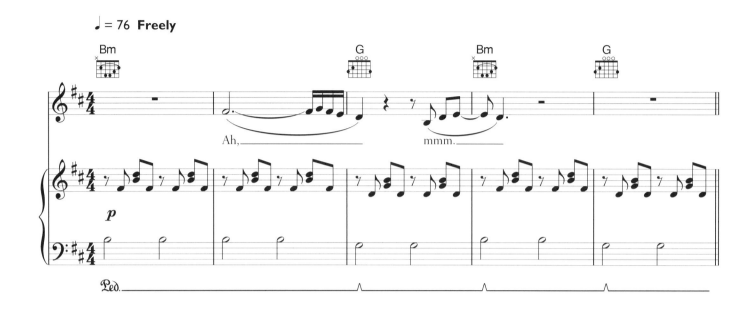

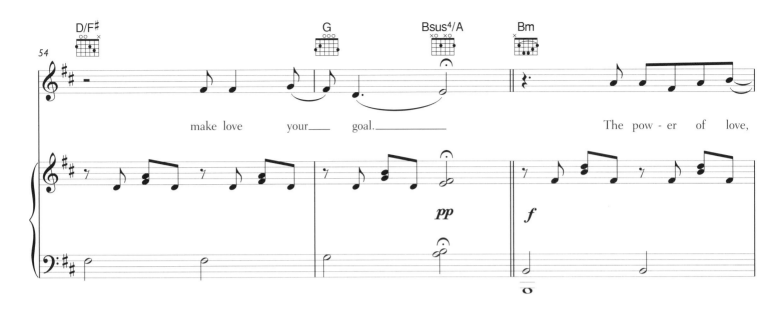

make love your goal. The pow-er of love,

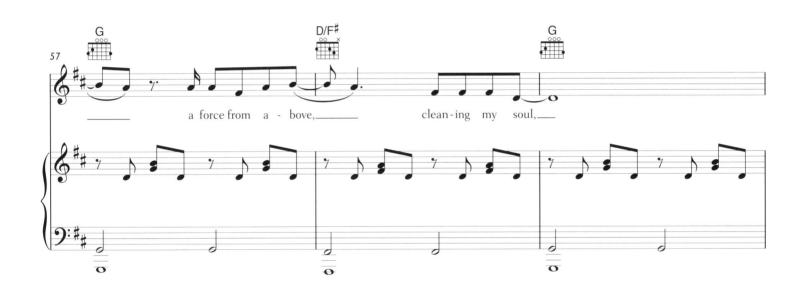

a force from a - bove, clean-ing my soul,

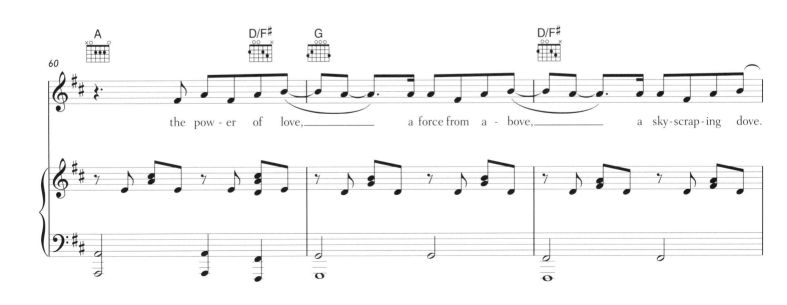

the pow - er of love, a force from a - bove, a sky-scrap-ing dove.

Flame on, burn de - sire,___ love with tongues of fire,_

___ purge the soul, make love your goal,___

make love your goal.

PRICE TAG

Words and Music by Claude Kelly, Bobby Ray Simmons Jr., Lukasz Gottwald and Jessica Cornish

NO SURPRISES

Words and Music by Thomas Yorke, Jonathan Greenwood,
Colin Greenwood, Edward O'Brien and Philip Selway

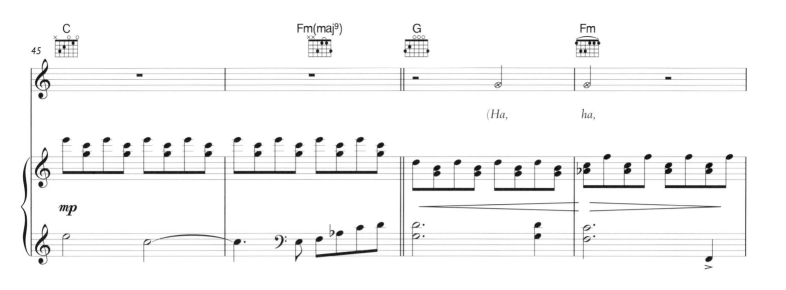

(Ha,   ha,

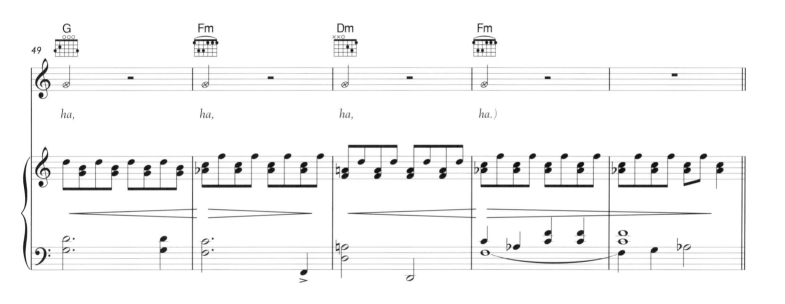

ha,   ha,   ha,   ha.)

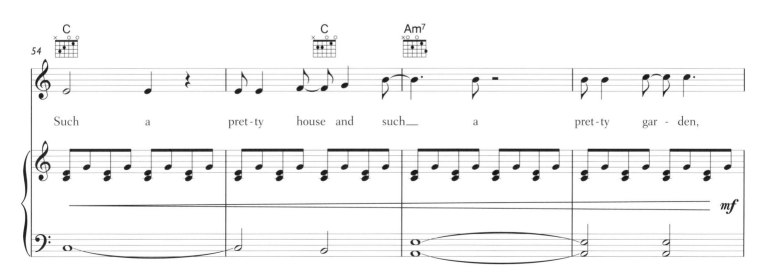

Such   a   pret-ty   house and   such___   a   pret-ty   gar - den,

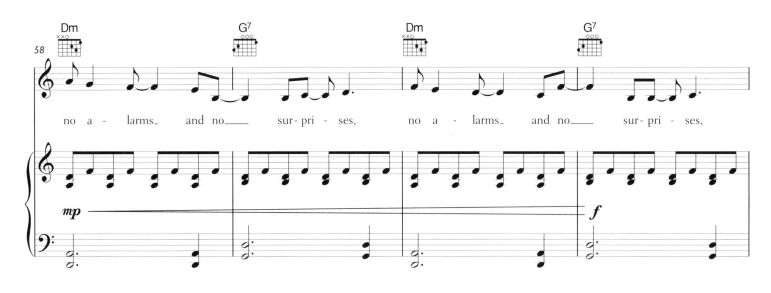

no a - larms_ and no____ sur - pri - ses, no a - larms_ and no____ sur - pri - ses,

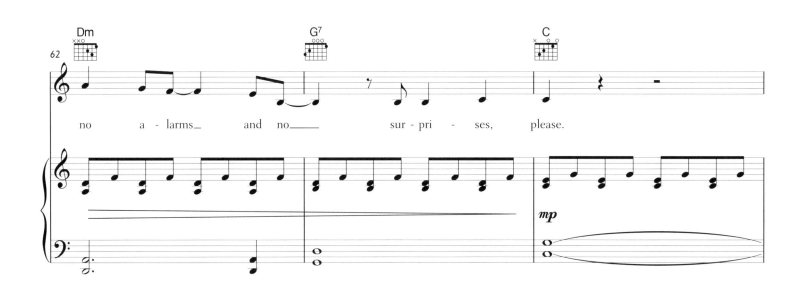

no a - larms_ and no____ sur - pri - ses, please.

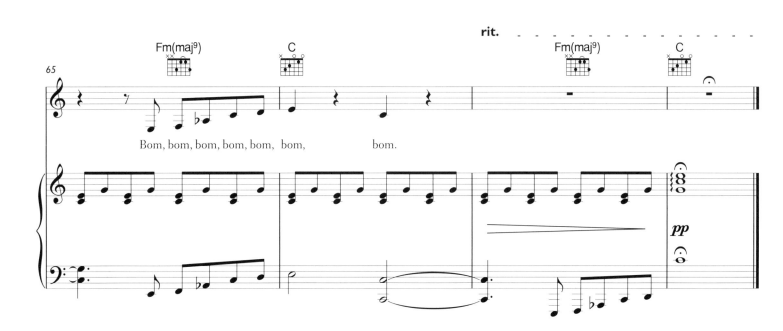

Bom, bom, bom, bom, bom, bom, bom.

(SITTIN' ON) THE DOCK OF THE BAY

Words and Music by Otis Redding and Steve Cropper

1. Sit-tin' in the morn-ing sun,___ I'll be sit-tin' when the eve-ning comes.
(2.) left my___ home___ in Geor-gia, head-ed for the 'Fris-co___ Bay.___
3. Sit-tin' here___ rest-ing my bones,___ and this lone-li-ness won't leave me a-lone,___

___ Watch-ing the ships roll in,___ and then I
___ 'Cause I've had___ nothing to live___ for, and look like
___ listen, two thou-sand miles I roam___ just to

STRONG

Words and Music by Hannah Reid, Dominic Major and Daniel Rothman

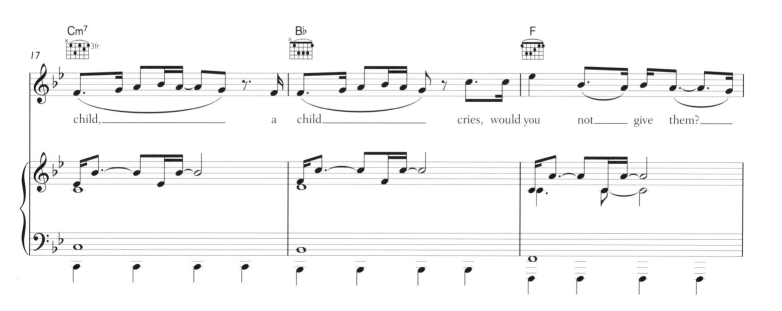

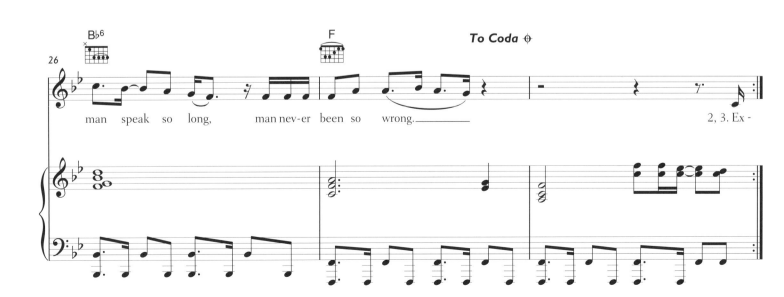

TOUCH THE SKY (FROM 'BRAVE')

Words by Alex Mandel and Mark Andrews
Music by Alex Mandel

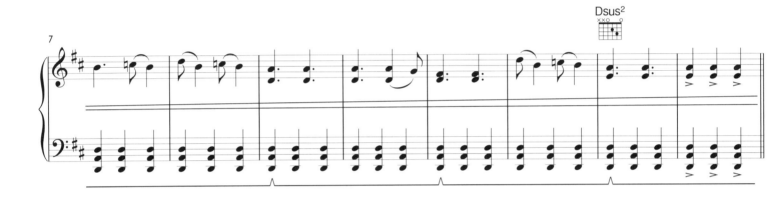

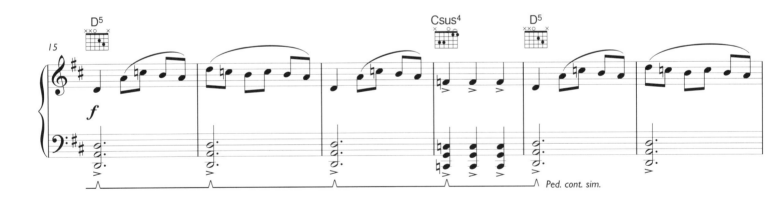

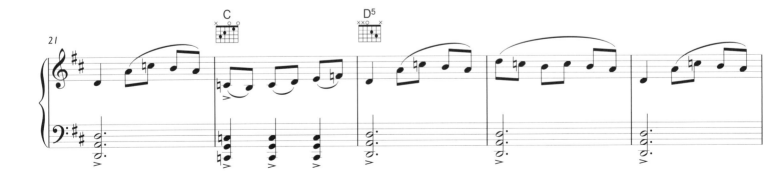

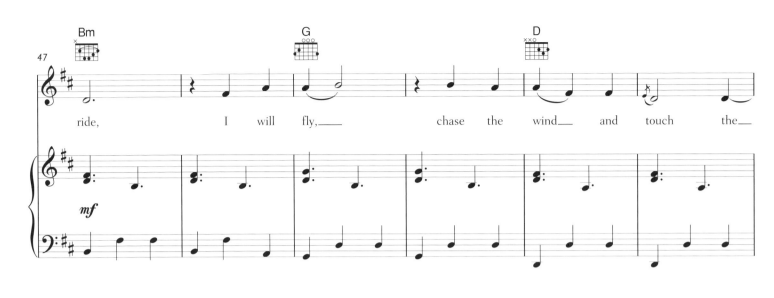

ride, I will fly,____ chase the wind____ and touch the____

____ sky, I will fly,____ chase the wind____ and touch the____

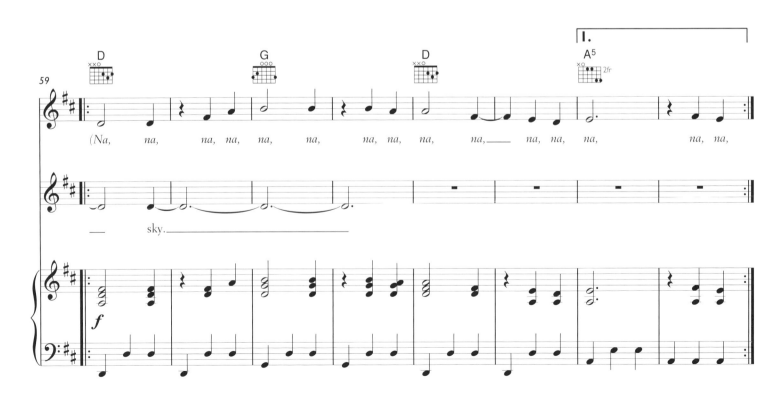

(Na, na, na, na, na, na, na, na, na, na,____ na, na, na, na, na,

____ sky._____

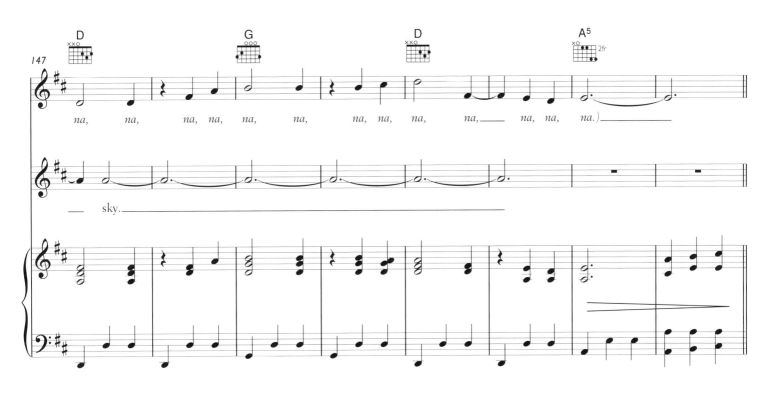

na, na, na, na, na, na, na, na, na, na, na, na, na.)

sky.

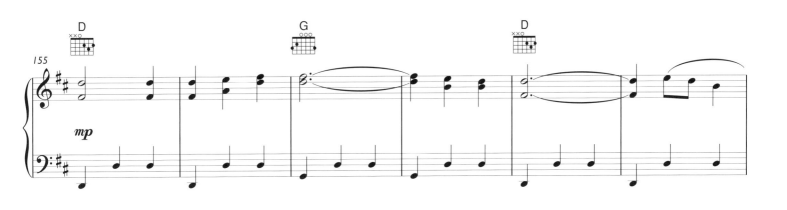

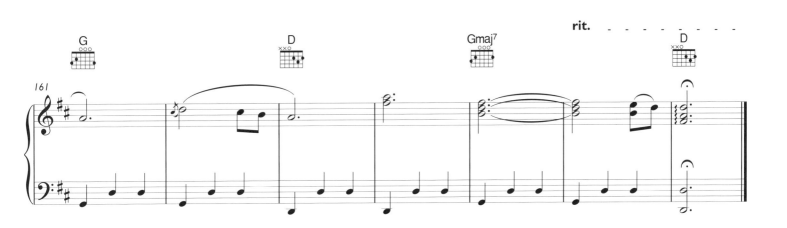

TURN YOUR FACE

Words and Music by Priscilla Hamilton and Steve Mac

UPRISING

Words and Music by Matthew Bellamy

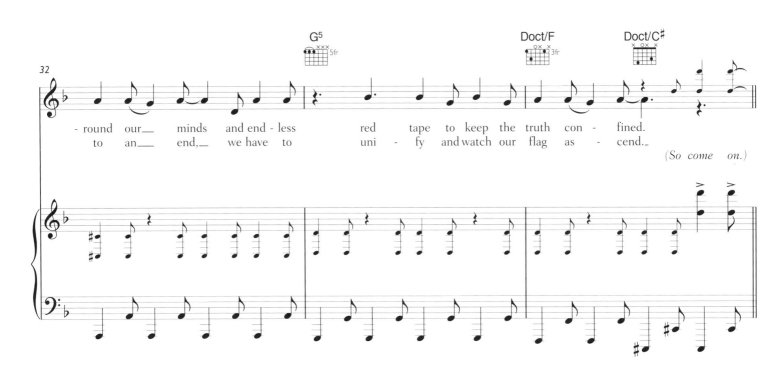

✛ *Coda*

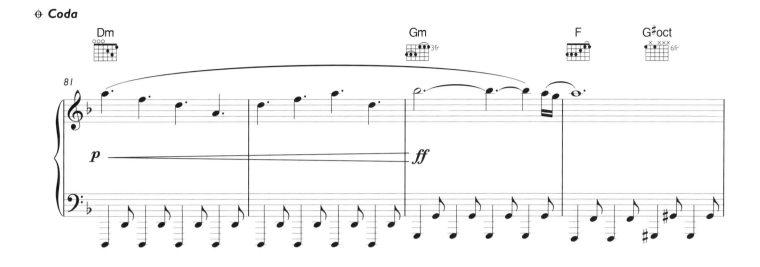

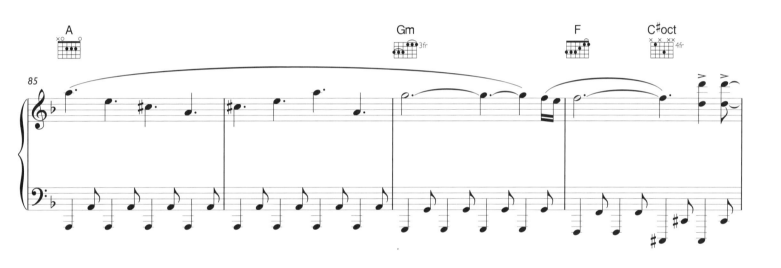

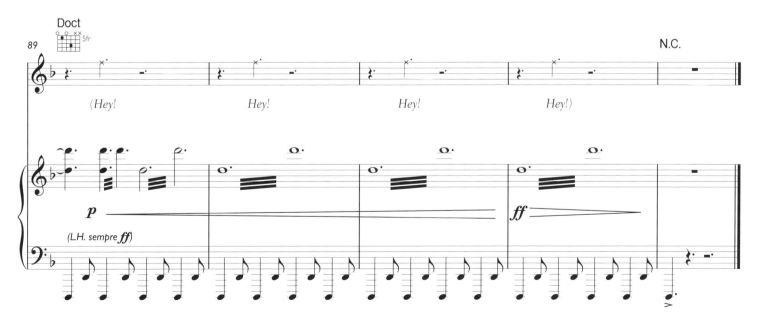

YOU'VE GOT A FRIEND IN ME (FROM 'TOY STORY')

Words and Music by Randy Newman

TOO CLOSE

Words and Music by Jim Duguid and Alex Clare

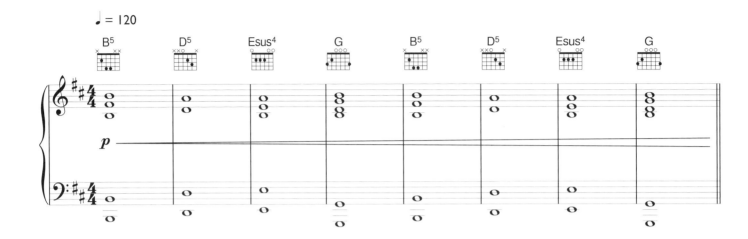

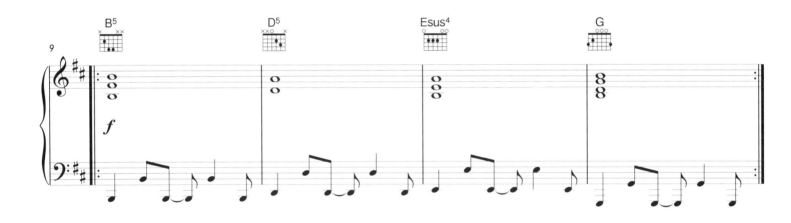

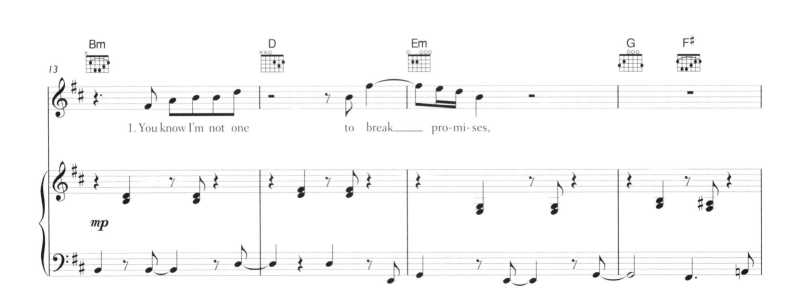

1. You know I'm not one to break pro‑mi‑ses,

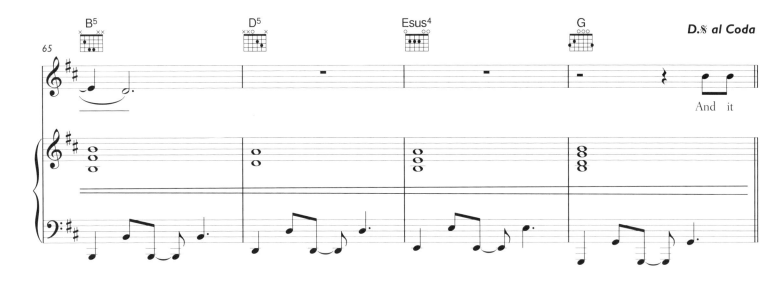

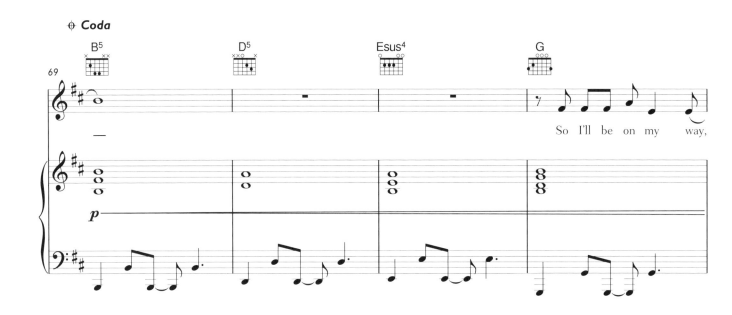

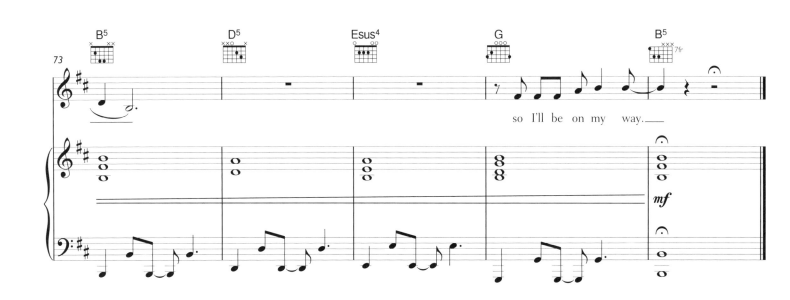

PIANO SONGBOOKS
FROM FABER MUSIC

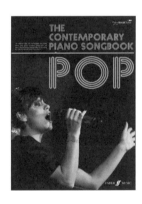  

Alicia Keys	0-571-53332-9	Nat King Cole	0-571-53217-9
Christmas	0-571-53563-1	Nina Simone Volume 1	0-571-52863-5
Classic Songs	0-571-52899-6	Nina Simone Volume 2	0-571-53035-4
Contemporary Piano Pop	0-571-53590-9	Norah Jones	0-571-53003-6
Contemporary Songs	0-571-52581-4	Radiohead	0-571-53448-1
Contemporary Songs 2	0-571-52888-0	Rock 'n' Roll	0-571-52988-7
Contemporary Songs 3	0-571-53211-X	Songs from the Movies	0-571-53549-6
Jazz	0-571-53166-0	Soul	0-571-53449-X

To buy Faber Music publications or to find out about the full range of titles available
please contact your local music retailer or Faber Music sales enquiries:

Faber Music Ltd, Burnt Mill, Elizabeth Way, Harlow CM20 2HX
Tel: +44 (0) 1279 82 89 82   Fax: +44 (0) 1279 82 89 83
sales@fabermusic.com   fabermusicstore.com